THE

DAILY SPARK

180 easy-to-use lessons and class activities!

THE DAILY SPARK

Critical Thinking
Critical Writing
Great Books
Journal Writing
Math Word Problems
Poetry
Pre-Algebra
SAT English
Shakespeare
Spanish
Spelling & Grammar
U.S. History
Vocabulary
Writing

THE

DAILY SPARK

Critical Writing

SPARK PUBLISHING

SPARKNOTES is a registered trademark of SparkNotes LLC.

Spark Publishing
A Division of Barnes & Noble Publishing
120 Fifth Avenue
New York, NY 10011
www.sparknotes.com

ISBN-13: 978-1-4114-9977-5
ISBN-10: 1-4114-9977-8

Please submit changes or report errors to www.sparknotes.com/errors.

Printed and bound in Canada.

Written by Ann Crowther and Jessica Allen.

Introduction

The *Daily Spark* series gives teachers an easy way to transform downtime into productive time. Most of the 180 exercises—one for each day of the school year—will take students ten to twenty minutes to complete. The exercises in this book may be photocopied and handed out to the class, projected as a transparency, or even read aloud. In addition to class time use, they can be assigned as homework exercises or extra-credit problems.

We've included some sample essay topics, which will give students an opportunity to practice timed essay-writing for the SAT and the ACT. Other prompts require students to use or refer to additional materials. Please consider providing students with a selection of magazines, academic journals, and newspapers for reference.

Use the *Daily Spark* to help your students become better critical writers. Each exercise in the *Critical Writing Daily Spark* encourages students to think of writing as a series of activities. Whether students are filling in the blanks with adjectives or adverbs, generating claims, rewriting bad paragraphs, or creating their own arguments to the man, they will always be developing the skills that lead to strong critical thinking, reading, and writing.

Spark your students' interest with the *Critical Writing Daily Spark*!

v

So Many Arguments

Different types of writing demand different types of claims. Write an arguable claim for two of the following types of argumentative essays:

- A compare-and-contrast essay about two movies

- An analytical essay about your favorite novel

- A definition essay about friendship

- A cause-and-effect essay about the relationship between driving to school and being late for class

Why We Score High

Cause-and-effect essays persuade readers of a particular argument by showing the relationships between people, events, trends, or historical circumstances. A cause-and-effect essay might argue that car emissions destroy trees or that excessive air-conditioning leads to lower productivity in the work place.

Imagine that you need to write an essay about the recent rise in SAT scores at your high school. Working backward, speculate on some of the causes of the higher test scores.

I Value Your Claims

In critical writing, a **claim** is the main point you're trying to assert or argue. There are four types of claims:

- A **claim of fact** states something that can be proven to be true or untrue: Extraterrestrial life exists.
- A **claim of value** states that something has or lacks worth: Animation is as important an art form as painting.
- A **claim of policy or solution** states an opinion about whether something ought to be done: All seniors should be given the opportunity to graduate in January.
- A **claim of cause and effect** makes inferences about the relationship between two or more actions or occurrences: Listening to hip-hop leads to higher SAT scores.

Write five claims of value.

Allow Me to Introduce You

The **introduction** of your essay has two main purposes: to introduce readers to your topic and to present readers with your main claim, which you will spend the remainder of the essay arguing, analyzing, and defending. Readers generally expect to find your main claim at the end of your introduction, but sometimes you might need to give two or three paragraphs of background, especially in longer papers, before presenting your main claim.

Write an introductory paragraph that ends with the claim The United States should lower the drinking age to eighteen.

I Claim to Have a Solution

In critical writing, a **claim** is the main point you're trying to assert or argue. There are four types of claims:

- A **claim of fact** states something that can be proven to be true or untrue: Extraterrestrial life exists.
- A **claim of value** states that something has or lacks worth: Animation is as important an art form as painting.
- A **claim of policy or solution** states an opinion about whether something ought to be done: All seniors should be given the opportunity to graduate in January.
- A **claim of cause and effect** makes inferences about the relationship between two or more actions or occurrences: Listening to hip-hop leads to higher SAT scores.

Write five claims of policy or solution.

Eggplant, Purple, Lumpily

Can you name the eight **parts of speech**? If you need help, check out the list below:

- **noun**: a person, place, thing, or idea (*chicken, dancehall, ocean, belief*)
- **pronoun**: replaces a noun (*he, she, it, her, them, who, which*)
- **adjective**: describes a noun or pronoun (*lovely, tattered, obese, violet*)
- **verb**: an action word (*ransack, stir, rejuvenate, are*)
- **adverb**: modifies or describes an adjective, verb, or other adverb (*gladly, helpfully, subtly, slowly*)
- **preposition**: links nouns and pronouns to phrases (*over, under, in, near*)
- **conjunction**: links lists, phrases, and clauses (*and, but, or, when*)
- **interjection**: conveys emotion (*wow, what, ouch, man*)

Write four sentences, in which you use all eight parts of speech. The catch? You can't use any part of speech more than once.

Fly Like a Bird

Think carefully about the issue presented in the following quotation from Helen Keller.

"One can never consent to creep when one feels an impulse to soar."

What is your view on the above statement? Plan and write an essay in which you develop your point of view on this issue. Support your stand with examples from your studies or experiences.

The Courageous Life

Think carefully about the issue presented in the following quotation from American writer Anaïs Nin.

"Life shrinks or expands in proportion to one's courage."

What is your view on the above statement? Plan and write an essay in which you develop your point of view on this issue. Support your stand with examples from your studies or experiences.

Comma, Comma, Comma

Commas have lots of uses, including:

- Telling readers to stop and pause: For me, broccoli is the bee's knees.

- Separating items in lists: Sara needs soap, staples, and Salisbury steak.

- Setting off introductory clauses: Feeding his fish, Freddie felt fine.

- Enclosing parenthetical elements: Joy, their stepmother, works in real estate.

Write four sentences that use commas correctly.

For Every Effect, a Cause

In critical writing, a **claim** is the main point you're trying to assert or argue. There are four types of claims:

- A **claim of fact** states something that can be proven to be true or untrue: Extraterrestrial life exists.
- A **claim of value** states that something has or lacks worth: Animation is as important an art form as painting.
- A **claim of policy or solution** states an opinion about whether something ought to be done: All seniors should be given the opportunity to graduate in January.
- A **claim of cause and effect** makes inferences about the relationship between two or more actions or occurrences: Listening to hip-hop leads to higher SAT scores.

Write five claims of cause and effect.

In the Beginning

Many readers consider your **introduction** to be the most important paragra~~~
essay. After all, the introduction hooks readers in and forces them to decide whethu.
continue reading.

Never begin your essays with clichéd or simplistic statements like *Since time began,
people have loved stories.* This wastes time and space. Instead, follow this formula for
good introductions:

- Provide interesting, but basic, background material and context for your
  discussion.
- Discuss your purpose for writing. Let your readers know why your essay
  matters and why your essay is relevant.
- Conclude your introduction with your main claim or thesis statement.
- Consider opening with an anecdote, quotation, question, or opinion.

Write a brief introduction for an argumentative essay about why we should abandon the
use of standardized tests like the SAT and the ACT in the college admissions process. **11**

arely Bracketed

metimes you'll need to change a word or two to make a quotation fit grammatically with the est of your sentence. Enclose the new letters, words, or phrases in **square brackets**. Use **ellipsis marks** to indicate omitted words.

Say you'd like to quote the first line of Jane Austen's *Pride and Prejudice* in your essay: It is a truth universally acknowledged, that a single man in possession of a good fortune must be in want of a wife. You might amend the line as follows: Austen's narrator claims that "a single [rich] man ... want[s] ... a wife."

Be careful about amending quotations too much. If you find that you must radically alter a quote to make it fit in with your ideas or sentences, change your ideas and sentences rather than changing the quote. A little alteration goes a long way, but too much alteration leaves your readers wondering why you would pick a quote that didn't quite fit in with your essay.

Make up at least one quotation about video games and work that quotation into a short paragraph about whether video games improve the IQs of their users.

DAILY SPARK · CRITICAL WRITING

Economics of Ethnicity

Think carefully about the issue presented in the following quotation from English writer Angela Carter.

"Racism cannot be separated from capitalism."

What is your view on the above statement? Plan and write an essay in which you develop your point of view on this issue. Support your stand with examples from your studies or experiences.

Some Friend

Think carefully about the issue presented in the following quotation from English writer Oscar Wilde.

"A true friend stabs you in the front."

What is your view on the above statement? Plan and write an essay in which you develop your point of view on this issue. Support your stand with examples from your studies or experiences.

Yea Becomes Nay Becomes Yea

Critical writing tries to persuade readers of the validity of an arguable claim. A big part of convincing readers is showing them that you, the writer, understand all sides of an issue. In other words, you need to address **counterarguments**. Your writing needs to present the other side(s) of an argument and then show why your position is the correct one.

Think about your views on high school government. Are you a *yea* or a *nay*? As a brain-stretching exercise, argue the opposite of your views in a short paragraph. If you're pro-government, argue against it, and if you're anti-government, pretend you're for it for a while.

Three Cheers for Democracy

Think carefully about the issue presented in the following quotation from Thomas Jefferson.

"That government is best which governs least, because its people govern themselves."

What is your view on the above statement? Plan and write an essay in which you develop your point of view on this issue. Support your stand with examples from your studies or experiences.

Let the Argument Begin

Critical writing requires **arguable claims**. But how do you know if your claim is arguable?

Every time you write a claim, give it the **reasonable person test**—that is, could a reasonable person argue your claim? Could a reasonable person also take the opposing view and make a convincing argument? If you answer *yes* to these questions, then you've got yourself an arguable claim.

Arguable claims must:

- Persuade their readers of something, get their readers to rethink something, or ask their readers to do something.
- Present a position or view that reasonable people could disagree with.
- Address a complex issue or try to answer a complex question.

Write two **arguable claims**: one about transportation and one about education.

Claim for Sale

Want readers to take your side? They'll only take your side—sometimes called **buying the claim**—if you give them enough evidence and explanation to support your views.

Imagine you're a journalist doing an exposé on plastic surgery. What kind of evidence would you introduce to convince readers that plastic surgery is wrong? Where would you find this evidence?

DAILY SPARK CRITICAL WRITING

Everyone Needs a Purpose

When writing, always consider your purpose—that is, always remind yourself why you're writing. The purpose of critical writing is often **to inform** (to shed light on a topic), **to convince** (to prove a point), or **to persuade** (to change readers' thoughts and spur them to action).

Imagine you have to make an argument about recent tuition increases at the local state university. What would be the purpose of your essay—to inform, to convince, or to persuade—if your audience consisted of students? What if your audience consisted of senior citizens or teachers? Write a short paragraph in which you explain how the purpose of your essay might change, given these three different audiences.

Ultimate Frisbee Now!

Refining your argument takes time, patience, and, usually, a few drafts. Imagine that you want to start an ultimate Frisbee team at your high school. Obviously you'll need to convince kids to join. But the adults at your school will also need to be persuaded. You'll have to prove to administrators that the team would attract students, that these students would be safe, and that the administrators should give you some money for equipment and jerseys.

Now you have a position: there should be an ultimate Frisbee team. You also have two potential audiences: fellow students and high school administrators. Pick an audience and brainstorm some claims and evidence to persuade that particular audience that there should be an ultimate Frisbee team at your school.

Be Prepared

Arguable claims need to be complex, original, and specific. One way to narrow down broad claims is to add specific information, connections, and reasons. To add complexity to your claims, try emphasizing connections that require a lot of explanation. Good claims encourage readers to read your essay to see how those connections work.

Make the following claims more specific and more complex:

- American high schools do not adequately prepare students for college.
- The drinking age should be changed.

Don't Act Passively

Does your own writing put you to sleep? If your writing seems dull, you might be using the **passive voice** too much.

In the passive voice, subjects receive the action:

The ball was hit over the fence, and a home run was scored.

In the **active voice**, the subject performs the action:

Jana hit the ball over the fence and scored a home run.

As a brain-stretching exercise, using only the passive voice, write a paragraph about something you did recently.

Evidently That's Evidence

All kinds of stuff counts as **evidence** in critical writing: facts, figures, expert opinions, maps, data, memoirs, quotations from the text, descriptions, illustrations, legal opinions, handwriting analysis, biographies, and so on. But while you can use practically anything as evidence, your evidence must relate to and support your arguable claims.

Your school newspaper has asked you to write a column in which you argue that the traditional 180-day school year should be abolished. Instead, a year-round 365-day school year should be instituted. Make a list of the types of evidence that you could reasonably include in your column.

Different Is Good

Different types of writing demand different types of claims. Write an arguable claim for two of the following types of essays:

- An inquiry or exploration essay about socks

- An evaluation essay about computers

- A narrative essay about your grandparents

- A descriptive essay about soda

Oui! I Mean Non!

Revise and edit the paragraph below. Remember to correct grammar mistakes and typos, vary sentence structure, eliminate qualifiers and intensifiers, rewrite logical fallacies, use topic and concluding sentences, and employ figurative language.

Every teen ager shouldn't have to learn so many foreign languages in school. English is the most spoken language there is, so why should we bother learning other languages? France doesn't hardly even have any power anymore, so why should we have to learn Frnech? Its not like were all going to go to France someday. Oui! I mean Non! Spanish makes more sense because the United States is so close to Mexico and other countries wear they speak Spanish, but even in those places most people speak English and deal with Americans. In a world where most people want to speak like Americans, we shouldn't ry to speak like other people.

An Audience of Many

As you're writing, always consider your **audience**, or readers. Who are they? What do they know? What do they believe? What do they value? What evidence or reasons will they find compelling?

Imagine you're writing an essay addressed to your fellow students. Make a list of the beliefs, values, knowledge, and characteristics that these students share. Then imagine you're writing an essay for the parents of students at your school. Make a list of the beliefs, values, knowledge, and characteristics that these parents share.

So What?

Critical writing requires claims, evidence, and analysis. Without analysis, your readers won't be able to understand how your evidence supports your claim or why you've chosen to include one piece of evidence over another.

One way to make sure that you've clearly explained the relationship between your evidence and your claims is to ask **so what**? Ask yourself, why have I included this evidence? What's my point? Why am I telling this to my readers? Your answers to these questions are part of your analysis—and therefore you should work your answers into your essay.

Write a short paragraph in which you make an argument about animal rights. Make sure your paragraph contains an arguable claim, at least one piece of evidence, and plenty of answers to *so what*?

But My Grandpop Herman Said....

Readers need lots of **evidence** to be persuaded of a claim. That's why it's called *argumentative writing*: as the writer, you are *arguing* a claim and trying to *persuade* readers to take your side. Readers won't take your side unless you give them a ton of evidence, but not all evidence is created equal.

Brainstorm a list of appropriate evidence for use in an argumentative academic essay. Your list might include encyclopedia articles but probably won't include the wisdom of your grandpop, smart as he may be.

I'll Starve, Thanks

An **either/or fallacy** is a logical fallacy in which the writer claims that there are only two possible outcomes to a complex situation. This type of fallacy usually requires readers to choose between the writer's argument and a horrible, untenable alternative. For example, a parent might tell a child, "Eat this liver-and-onion omelet or starve." The parent might then laugh maniacally.

Write three statements in which you commit the either/or fallacy.

This Argument Sinks!

As a brain-stretching exercise, write a paragraph in support of the claim below without citing a single statistic, quoting a single expert opinion, defining any term, or giving any shred of evidence.

If the pool committee hires more lifeguards, pool fees will increase yet again, driving away many longtime poolgoers.

You Bank Robber, You

A **complex**, or **loaded**, **question** is a logical fallacy in which the writer asks two questions in one or asks a question that implies an unsupported assumption.

Here's an example:

Where did you go after you robbed the bank?

In this case, there is a question asked (where did you go?) and an assumption made (you robbed the bank).

Write three complex questions.

Read a Book, Book a Trip

Equivocation is a logical fallacy in which the writer uses a word with two or more definitions in order to confuse or trick the reader:

> Artists use paint, and houses get painted. Therefore, artists paint houses.

In this illogical example, the writer plays with the word *paint*, using it first as a noun and then as a verb in order to come to a conclusion about the relationship between artists and houses.

To avoid equivocating in your writing, list five words that have at least two meanings.

Birth-Order Brainstorm

Brainstorming means listing all of the ideas related to a topic. When writers brainstorm, they don't worry about whether the ideas are plausible or even interesting. Instead, they just list everything they can possibly think of that might be relevant to their topic or argument.

When you're brainstorming, write down everything that comes to mind, even if it seems silly or stupid. You never know which ideas might actually work.

In the next five minutes, brainstorm on the topic of birth order.

The Man Walked the Cat in a Tie

Misplaced modifiers cause confusion and consternation in your readers. Observe:

Rushing for some catnip treats, the stacks of books were overturned by Gertrude the cat.

Right now, the sentence implies that the stacks of books were rushing for some catnip treats. The sentence should read:

Rushing for some catnip treats, Gertrude the cat overturned the stacks of books.

As a brain-stretching exercise, write three sentences with misplaced modifiers. Then rewrite your sentences, correctly placing all modifiers.

A Shocking Haircut

Faulty causation, also called the **post hoc fallacy**, is a logical fallacy in which the writer makes an illogical assumption about what caused something. When one event or thing occurs immediately after another event or thing, people often wrongly assume that the first event caused the second.

Here's an example:

> Maple got a shock right after she came home from the hair salon. Therefore, Maple should never go to the hair salon again.

Write three statements that rely on faulty causation.

mple Questions

mple **questions** is another great way to brainstorm. Remember the six key questions of journalists: who?, what?, when?, where?, why?, and how? These questions can help you figure out how to target your research and how to plan your essay. They can also help you suss out interesting ideas.

In the next five minutes, think of a significant event in world history. Then answer these six questions with regard to the event.

Everywhere, Arguments

We make arguments all the time without realizing it. For instance, when was the last time you tried to convince your friends to go see a certain movie with you? You probably tried to persuade them to come by telling them about the great actors and cool special effects or soundtrack, or maybe you even offered to drive or pay for their tickets. Likewise, a kid who tries to convince her parents to buy her a new pair of sneakers must make an argument. She might hold up her ratty old sneakers as evidence of her need for a new pair, or she might claim that she needs new kicks for a sports team.

Make a list of five nonacademic arguments you've made in the last month.

Don't Be So Hasty

Faulty, or **hasty**, **generalizations** are logical fallacies in which the writer makes general statements without giving enough evidence to prove that the statements are true. Essentially, people make faulty generalizations when they jump to conclusions.

Stereotypes and prejudices are the result of faulty generalizations. Here's an example:

> Stefanie and Jamie are obnoxious and rude soccer players. Tina and Beth play soccer. They're probably loud and mean, too.

Write three statements that rely on faulty generalizations.

Nothing Compares to....

A **false analogy** is a logical fallacy in which the writer makes a comparison between two unrelated things or situations. Often, writers make false analogies because they don't have all of the information, they overlook some important piece of information, or they generalize from superficial similarities. For example, students who compare high school to prison make a false analogy.

Write three statements in which you make a false analogy.

Emotions of Arguments

In an **appeal to emotion**, writers attempt to invoke emotions in their readers in order to convince those readers of a claim. For example, an argumentative essay about the death penalty might include anecdotes from the families of victims of violent crimes. An argumentative essay about stricter immigration laws might appeal to fear by convincing readers that they are in danger of losing their jobs to illegal immigrants.

Write five persuasive sentences that appeal to emotion.

Donkey, Elephant, or Independent

Unlike brainstorming, in which writers make lists, **freewriting** means writing without stopping for a certain amount of time. When writers freewrite, they don't worry about grammar, spelling, mechanics, or word choice. Instead, they just write. The idea is to write whatever comes to mind, without worrying or censoring yourself. Freewriting is a great way to get the writing juices flowing when you're feeling stuck or blocked.

For the next five minutes, freewrite on the topic of school lunches.

Inquiring Minds....

An **inquiry** or **exploration essay** might summarize a topic, explain a controversy, or explore a subject that your readers don't know much about. In this type of essay, the writer writes objectively, rather than subjectively taking a stance on an issue or topic. Sometimes writers write inquiry or exploration essays as the first draft of an **argumentative essay**, in which they take a side and argue a point of view.

Examples of inquiry or exploration essays include a profile discussing the experiences of a member of the New York Police Department and a description of the hotels in Madrid, Spain.

List six topics or controversies that you would enjoy researching for an inquiry or exploration essay.

As Everyone Knows

In an **appeal to common sense**, writers emphasize the good judgment and common sense of their readers in order to persuade them of something. An argumentative essay that appeals to common sense might use phrases like *as everyone knows* and *as any rational person can see*.

Write five persuasive sentences that appeal to common sense.

First One Thing, Then the Other

A **non sequitur** is a logical fallacy in which the writer makes a conclusion or statement that doesn't logically relate to the previous statement. For example, when a writer switches topics in the middle of an essay, he or she commits a non sequitur. Another non sequitur: the president of a corporation praises his employees' productivity but then claims that the conference room needs more plants.

Write three non sequiturs.

An Illogical Fish

A **red herring** is a logical fallacy in which the writer changes the subject of an argument by introducing a topic that has little or no relevance to the argument. For example, an essay might begin by arguing that students should be allowed to park in the faculty parking lot but might conclude by arguing against buying hybrid cars.

Make a list of the various red herrings you could throw into an argument about the following topics:

- Pollution
- Health care
- Welfare reform
- Bag searches on public transportation

This One Time....

Anecdotes are very brief stories told to illustrate a point. Narrative essays are full of anecdotes, but you also can use anecdotes in argumentative writing. A carefully selected anecdote or two can help you emphasize a claim or theme and can help you make a personal connection to your readers.

Imagine that you have been chosen to give the commencement speech at your high school graduation this year. What will you say? Write a short speech and include two anecdotes that help illustrate your main theme or idea.

Trust Me, I'm Virtuous

In an **appeal to ethics**, writers attempt to persuade their readers by highlighting their own good character or the supposed moral superiority of the position for which they are arguing. An argumentative essay that appeals to ethics might use phrases like *you can trust me* and *the virtuous position is*.

Write five sentences that appeal to ethics.

The Golden Argument

In an **appeal to tradition or custom**, writers use social conventions, beliefs, or behaviors to support their arguments. For instance, to remind students to clean up after themselves, teachers and cafeteria staff might invoke the Golden Rule: *Do unto others as you would have them do unto you.* An argumentative essay about politics might begin with the phrase, *As our forefathers once wrote....*

Write five persuasive sentences that appeal to tradition or custom.

Cottony, Lime Green Trousers

In a **descriptive essay**, writers describe a person, situation, trend, phenomenon, object, or topic. Like an inquiry or exploration essay, descriptive essays are often the first draft of an **argumentative essay**, in which the writer takes a side and argues a point of view.

Descriptive essays emphasize how things look, feel, smell, or taste. To invoke the senses, writers use especially colorful language and vivid descriptions.

Write a paragraph in which you describe the outfit you're wearing right now.

I Am Holden Caulfield

Lens essays make an argument by using one idea, situation, or phenomenon to magnify or examine another idea, situation, or phenomenon. Examples of lens essays include using the concept of natural selection from biology to argue that the best-adapted workers always rise to the top of the corporate ladder or using the economic concept of interest to describe how friendships grow over time.

Choose a theme from a literary work you have read in class this year and use it to make an argument about what you learned from a personal experience.

Sussing Out Sources

Critical writing often demands that you to do some research. For example, you might have to look up some information about your topic, define some key words, or find evidence to analyze. But not all sources are created equal.

Here's a checklist for evaluating sources:

- For books, look at the author and publisher. What kinds of credentials does the author have? Does the author seem knowledgeable? How widely known is the publisher? Have you heard of the author or publisher before?
- If you're using the internet, make sure that the source is credible. Check whether it is endorsed by a university or respectable authority. Does it cite other scholarly sources? Who posted the site, and who wrote most of the content? Are there frequent typographical errors and misspellings? Does the website seem old and out of date?

List at least two worthwhile sources for each of the following topics.

- Urban planning
- Do-it-yourself garden
- Nineteenth-century authors
- Sausage-making

You Try Arguing with a Scarecrow

A **straw-man fallacy** is a logical fallacy in which the writer tries to bolster his or her argument by making the opposing argument seem simplistic or silly. Readers won't trust writers who dismiss the other side quickly or thoughtlessly. Good writers treat opposing views and counterarguments with respect and careful consideration, even as these writers show why their view is the correct one.

Write a short paragraph about the graduation requirements at your school. Commit the straw-man fallacy at least once.

Everybody's Doing It

In an **appeal to populism**, writers attempt to persuade their readers by highlighting the popularity of their own position. An argumentative essay that uses an appeal to populism might, for example, use statistics to show that a majority of people favor the position of the writer. Another appeal to populism might cite an everyday Man on the Street or Average Joe who believes the same thing as the writer.

Write five sentences that appeal to populism.

Because the Experts Say So

Relying on **expert opinions** helps strengthen your argument. Readers trust experts, because experts are knowledgeable, honorable, and authoritative.

When citing an expert's opinion, you might consider giving some background information about your expert, especially if the expert might be unfamiliar to your audience: award-winning essayist Susan Sontag; presidential nominee John Kerry; winner of seventeen hot dog–eating contests H. Packard.

What kind of expert opinion could you cite to support each the following arguments?

- Eating ice cream helps people lose weight.
- Vote no on the proposed law against eating while driving. This law will harm people psychologically, rather than making people physically safe.
- An MBA degree does not lead to a job in the business world.

Solid As a Rock

Readers value **hard evidence**, such as statistics, case studies, and facts. In some disciplines, like the biological and social sciences, current and objective data matter more than any other type of evidence. Remember that you must explain the relationship between your evidence and your claim, regardless of the type of evidence you're using.

List two arguments that would require you to use hard evidence. Then list two arguments in which hard evidence might be out of place or unnecessary.

So Many Sources

There are two types of sources: primary and secondary. **Primary sources** include firsthand accounts, diaries, maps, data, literary texts, letters, and other original materials. **Secondary sources** analyze and interpret other works, articles, and materials, including primary sources. Examples of secondary sources include scientific reports, book reviews, scholarly articles, and biographies. The best evidence consists of a mix of primary and secondary sources.

Look at the following list of sources. Indicate which are primary sources and which are secondary sources.

- A painting
- An interview
- A performance of a symphony
- A historical commentary
- A train schedule
- A website about a historical figure
- A literary journal
- A collection of essays

Everyday Research

We **research** every day, even when we don't realize it. For example, checking out the movie listings on a website is a form of research, as is the kind of comparison shopping you might do to find the best deal on an iPod. Any time we go to a book, newspaper, magazine, website, person, or other type of source to find an answer to a question, we're doing research.

List ten types of research you've performed in the past week.

Some Rules Don't Rule

To make a **rough outline**, list your main ideas or topics in a logical order. Then list supporting details under each idea. If you want, use dashes to set off the details.

Here's a rough outline for an essay that argues against the use of identification cards in high schools:

ID Policy Is Tearing Schools Apart

Students don't respect teachers or administrators anymore.
- To many kids, it seems as though the faculty nag them for IDs.
- Some teachers don't bother with IDs; some teachers are cooler than others, since the ones who enforce the policy look bad to kids.

IDs are taking away from instruction.
- Teachers are checking IDs when they should be teaching their subject matter.
- Kids often have to leave class to get their IDs.

Think about the rules and policies at your school. Pick one that you feel strongly about and write a rough outline for an essay in which you praise or criticize it.

Factually Opinionated

A fact is a statement that can be proven to be true. An opinion is something that a person believes or perceives. Both facts and opinions can appear in critical writing.

Here's a factual statement about an essay written for school:

My paper discusses Arthur Miller's *Death of a Salesman*.

Here's a statement of opinion about the same essay:

My paper makes an excellent argument about Miller's play.

To clarify the difference between facts and opinions, write two sentences about each of the following topics. One sentence should state a fact, and the other should state an opinion.

- Your favorite television show
- The last class you attended

A Lotta Love

Think carefully about the issue presented in the following quotation from Mother Theresa.

"We can do no great things—only small things with great love."

What is your view on the above statement? Plan and write an essay in which you develop your point of view on this issue. Support your stand with examples from your studies or experiences.

Do You Concede?

Making concessions, or acknowledging the validity of opposing claims, helps make your arguable claims more believable. Showing your readers that you've studied all aspects of an issue or argument makes you seem authoritative and thoughtful—and it makes readers more likely to trust you.

Imagine that you are writing an essay to support the following claim:

> As part of a meaningful civic education, high school students should be given the right to vote in school board elections.

Come up with one concession for each of the expressions listed below.

- Admittedly …
- Granted …
- Although …
- While it is true that …

Should you find yourself completely bewildered about how to begin your research, don't panic. Feeling overwhelmed at the start of a project is completely natural. Here are some tips for combating anxiety:

- Read and reread the assignment. Teachers pack valuable information into assignments, so pay attention to the verbs they use. What does the assignment ask you to do? The task that teachers want you to complete should determine how you go about doing research.
- Think about your audience. Who will be reading your essay? What does your audience need to know about your topic?
- Begin as generally as possible. Do a Google search. Doing something small and simple—like gathering preliminary information—can help you feel productive.

To get some practice doing research, pick a subject you'd like to learn more about—say scuba diving or Tasmania. If possible, go to the library or get online and find some information about the topic. If you can't hit the books or surf the web, imagine which sources you'd use to find out more about your subject. Write a short paragraph that summarizes your findings.

Just Don't Do It!

Plagiarism is the act of claiming someone else's work, ideas, or words as your own. Any time you use another person's work, ideas, or words without including some kind of acknowledgment or citation, you're committing plagiarism. You don't need to cite facts everybody knows or your own claims, research findings, or discoveries.

Whether you plagiarize intentionally (as in the case of a paper downloaded from the internet) or unintentionally (because of sloppy research techniques, for example), plagiarism is seen as stealing. Just don't do it. When in doubt, cite.

List five things you can do to avoid plagiarism.

High School Reality

You've been chosen to appear on *High School Reality*, a reality show about high school students, but you need parental consent. Unfortunately, your parents didn't want you to try out for the show and now they might not let you go—that is, unless you can convince them otherwise.

Write three specific claims to convince your parents to let you appear on *High School Reality*. Then list three pieces of evidence you could give to support those three claims.

Hire ME!

The **tone** of a text conveys the writer's attitude toward a subject. Readers uncover a writer's tone by looking at word choice, sentence structure, figurative language, and punctuation.

Imagine you've just found the job of your dreams. To apply, you need to write a business letter that sells yourself to the potential employer and explains why she should hire you over all of the other candidates. Write the letter, using an appropriate business tone and lots of evidence.

rown-Up Brainstorm

Brainstorming means listing all of the ideas related to a topic. When writers brainstorm, they don't worry about whether the ideas are plausible or even interesting. Instead, they just list everything they can possibly think of that might be relevant to their topic or argument.

When you're brainstorming, write down everything that comes to mind, even if it seems silly or stupid. You never know which ideas might actually work.

For the next five minutes, brainstorm all of the advantages and disadvantages of growing up.

Good Art, Bad Artists

Think carefully about the issue presented in the following quotation from American artist Georgia O'Keefe.

"Art is a wicked thing. It is what we are."

What is your view on the above statement? Plan and write an essay in which you develop your point of view on this issue. Support your stand with examples from your studies or experiences.

United States of Freewriting

Unlike brainstorming, in which writers make lists, **freewriting** means writing without stopping for a certain amount of time. When writers freewrite, they don't worry about grammar, spelling, mechanics, or word choice. Instead, they just write. The idea is to write whatever comes to mind, without worrying or censoring yourself. Freewriting is a great way to get the writing juices flowing when you're feeling stuck or blocked.

For the next five minutes, freewrite on racial and cultural unity. Is true unity possible in the United States?

Hometown Journal

Keeping a journal, or **journaling**, can help you figure out what you want to say about a topic or issue. Journaling is different from freewriting for two reasons: first, journaling asks you to write about yourself—your thoughts, your feelings, and your experiences. Second, journaling tends to be more focused than freewriting.

A journal entry might include specific details or might consist of a complete anecdote. A piece of freewriting, in contrast, might jump from topic to topic or might be completely nonsensical to anyone but you. In general, a journal entry is more polished than a piece of freewriting.

For the next ten minutes, journal about your hometown.

What's Your Favorite Color?

Performing research doesn't just mean going to the library and surfing the internet or thumbing through an encyclopedia. Sometimes research also involves **conducting interviews**. Direct quotations can add authority and weight to your writing.

Interviewers always plan out their interviews in advance. They think of a list of specific questions to ask their subject, including a mix of detailed and open-ended queries.

Imagine you've been asked to conduct an interview of your favorite celebrity for *People* magazine. Prepare a list of ten questions to ask.

DAILY SPARK · CRITICAL WRITING

Vroom-Vroom

Your state legislature has just proposed that having a high school diploma should be a prerequisite to getting a driver's license. A person would have to show proof of a diploma or a GED certificate before he or she could take the driving test. Outraged, you decide to write a letter urging the legislature to keep the driving age at seventeen, as it currently is. Your letter gives three reasons:

- Many high school students have part-time jobs. These students will be unable to commute from work to school, and they will have to quit their jobs.
- The proposed law seems to discriminate against new immigrants, especially those from poor countries who might not have had access to secondary education or who might not be able to prove that they have the equivalent of a U.S. diploma.
- This proposed law is unreasonable; there is no link between a high school degree and the safe handling of a car.

What kind of evidence would you need to support each reason? List at least one piece of evidence for each reason.

Wise Words

Think carefully about the issue presented in the following quotation from Oprah Winfrey.

"Follow your instincts. That's where true wisdom manifests itself."

What is your view on the above statement? Plan and write an essay in which you develop your point of view on this issue. Support your stand with examples from your studies or experiences.

Duly Noted

Taking notes involves picking out key points to summarize or paraphrase, as well as finding words or phrases to quote directly.

Here are some tips for taking good notes:

- Read the text without making any notes. After you've finished reading, write down your first impressions. What did you like? What didn't you like?
- Reread the text as an active reader. This time, make notes in the margins that sum up a paragraph in a word or two. Underline key points, words, or phrases.
- Write down any questions you might have. Reread the text until you've answered them all.

Choose a short article from a magazine, newspaper, or journal. Read the article a few times, taking notes as you go. Then write up a short summary of the article, using your notes as a guide.

Argue Man

An **argument to the man**, or **ad hominem attack**, is a logical fallacy in which the writer attacks the character of his or her opponent. Writers rely on this type of fallacy to distract readers from the issues at hand, as when one political candidate accuses another—without any evidence—of accepting bribes.

Write three arguments to the man.

Romantic Comedies Rule

Begging the question, also known as a **circular argument**, is a logical fallacy in which the writer acts as if an important issue has already been answered or addressed. When writers beg the question, they draw conclusions from reasons or assumptions that have not yet been supported or proven.

Here's an example:

> Romantic comedies are the best type of movie, because romantic comedies are better than horror movies, dramas, other comedies, and foreign films.

In this example, the writer restates the position of the first clause—that romantic movies are the best type of movie—in the second clause. Rather than explain why romantic movies rule, the writer simply reiterates that they do.

Write three statements in which you beg the question.

CRITICAL WR

Better Readers and Writers

Close reading helps you become a better reader and writer, because close reading forces you to pay attention to every aspect of a written text.

Here are some questions to ask yourself as you read:

- What's the work about?
- What's the work's purpose? To inform? To entertain? To persuade?
- Is the writing formal? Informal?
- What's the overall vocabulary used? A lot of long, polysyllabic words? Short, simple words?
- What types of words are used? Do the words follow a pattern?
- What types of sounds are used? Are words or sounds repeated?
- What do the sentences look like? Are any rules of grammar broken?
- What works for you as a reader? Are there any phrases that stick out as being memorable? Why? What do you like? What don't you like?

Pick a paragraph from an article or book. As you read, ask yourself these questions. Then formulate your answers into a paragraph.

The Source Says

One way to avoid plagiarism is by writing **summaries** of texts or portions of texts in your own words. To ensure that you use only your own words, keep the summary as brief as possible and do not look at the source text as you write. If you feel that you must use particular words or phrases from the source, put those words or phrases in quotation marks.

Remember that the source of your summary must be cited on a works cited page. Even though summaries don't include direct quotations, they do use the ideas and spirit of other works—which means they must be formally acknowledged in order to avoid plagiarism.

Practice your summarizing skills by reading and summarizing a magazine or newspaper article.

Tarred and Feathered

Like summaries, **paraphrases** give the spirit of a text without using direct quotations. Paraphrases tend to be as long as the original texts, and sometimes even longer. They also tend to more closely model original texts, unlike summaries, which simply give a brief synopsis.

When you paraphrase, you should write your own words, interpretations, and comments about a source text, but without that text in front of you as you write. As always, when you absolutely must quote from the source, remember to put the words in quotation marks. Also, remember that all paraphrases must be cited on your works cited page.

Write a brief paragraph in which you discuss the consequences you think plagiarists ought to face. Then switch papers with a classmate. Read your classmate's piece and write a paraphrase of his or her paragraph.

Open-Ended Argument

Imagine you've been assigned to write an argumentative essay on … anything
Rather than freak out, try thinking of this assignment as a chance to explore a topic that
interests you.

Here are some tips for deciding on a topic:

- Consider the length, deadline, and purpose of the project. Don't pick a topic
  that's too broad, such as sports, for a two-page paper that's due in a week.
- Make a list of subjects that fascinate you. What would you like to learn more about?
- What do you like to do in your spare time? What kinds of magazines and books do
  you like to read? What kinds of movies or television shows do you like to watch?
- Make a list of topics that you already feel comfortable with. Perhaps there's an
  aspect or element of a subject that you can explore in depth.

Using these tips, make a list of ten topics you'd be willing to develop into an argumentative
essay. Give a mix of broad and narrow topics.

Brainstorming means listing all of the ideas related to a topic. When writers brainstorm, they don't worry about whether the ideas are plausible or even interesting. Instead, they just list everything they can possibly think of that might be relevant to their topic or argument.

When you're brainstorming, write down everything that comes to mind, even if it seems silly or stupid. You never know which ideas might actually work.

For the next five minutes, brainstorm all of the ways your life would change if you stopped using electricity.

Yesterday I....

Keeping a journal, or **journaling**, can help you figure out what you want to say about a topic or issue. Journaling is different from freewriting for two reasons: first, journaling asks you to write about yourself—your thoughts, your feelings, and your experiences. Second, journaling tends to be more focused than freewriting.

A journal entry might include specific details or might consist of a complete anecdote. A piece of freewriting, in contrast, might jump from topic to topic or might be completely nonsensical to anyone but you. In general, a journal entry is more polished than a piece of freewriting.

For the next ten minutes, journal about something that happened to you yesterday.

Choose Your Argument

Think of a logical fallacy that might be found in each of the following essays:

- An essay arguing for healthier menu choices in the school cafeteria
- An essay against a town curfew for teens
- An essay in favor of stricter gun control laws
- An essay with the argument of your choice

Hey Good Lookin', Nice Soul

Think carefully about the issue presented in the following quotation from German philosopher Ludwig Wittgenstein.

"The face is the body of the soul."

What is your view on the above statement? Plan and write an essay in which you develop your point of view on this issue. Support your stand with examples from your studies or experiences.

Order Up an A

There are many ways to set up, or **organize**, an argumentative essay. How **you present your** evidence helps your readers understand and follow your argument.

Here are some useful ways of ordering your evidence:

- Chronological order
- Order of importance
- Quality-by-quality order (discuss one quality of an idea or subject, then move on to the next quality, and so on)
- Cause-and-effect order

How would you order the following pieces of writing?

- An essay about the mood of a painting
- A manual called "How to Be a Model Student"
- An essay comparing cars in 1950 to cars today
- An essay discussing the meaning of the color yellow in *The Yellow Wallpaper*

No Computers Allowed

Many writers end their paragraphs with a **concluding sentence**. This sentence sums up the main idea of the paragraph and reminds readers of how the paragraph supports and connects to the essay's overarching claim.

Write a paragraph that argues that computers should not be allowed in high school classrooms. Make sure your paragraph acts like an essay—that is, make sure your paragraph has a topic sentence, an arguable claim, evidence, analysis, and a concluding sentence.

Liberty for All or None

Think carefully about the issue presented in the following quotation from American writer Thomas Paine.

> "He that would make his own liberty secure must guard even his enemy from oppression; for if he violates this duty he establishes a precedent that will reach to himself."

What is your view on the above statement? Plan and write an essay in which you develop your point of view on this issue. Support your stand with examples from your studies or experiences.

Not Dressed for Success

Revise and edit the paragraph below. Remember to correct grammar mistakes and typos, vary sentence structure, eliminate qualifiers and intensifiers, rewrite logical fallacies, use topic and concluding sentences, and employ figurative language.

School dress codes are just about the worst idea of all time. They suck! You have to spend all this dough on scratchy uniforms that don't look good. Talk about unflattering, the skirts make girls into big blobs and the ties make boys look like security goons. The scratchiness makes it hard to concentrate, because we're always like scratching isnstead of wattching the teacher. We shouldn't have school dres scdoes. We shoudl be allowed to dresss how we want. Because we will have to dress how we want once we graduate.

Should I Stay or Should I Quote?

Deciding when to paraphrase and when to quote directly can sometimes be difficult. Although including some quotations from primary and secondary sources will make you seem like an authoritative writer, stringing together quotation after quotation will make you seem lazy and incapable of making an original argument.

Here are a few questions to consider when deciding whether to quote or paraphrase:

- **Is the language in the quote unusual or lively?** Will it add oomph to your essay?
- **Is the writer an authority on the issue in question?** Quoting authorities shows your readers that you've done research and know something about your topic.
- **Is your essay about a literary work, article, or historical event?** If so, you need to quote directly from the work, article, or primary source related to the event.

Imagine you're writing an argumentative essay about steroids in sports. List some people you might want to quote directly, and list some people or sources you might prefer to paraphrase. Feel free to make up names and professions.

Coco and Auden

Signal words help readers understand your reasons for including a quotation, summary, or paraphrase. These words help integrate the ideas from the primary or secondary source with the main ideas of your essay. Quotations, summaries, and paraphrases must always be introduced—you can't just stick them into your essay and hope your readers follow along.

Here's an example of signal words in action:

> As Dr. Coco asserts daily on different talk shows, relationships don't heal themselves. People must work together to understand one another. W. H. Auden expressed a similar idea when he wrote, "We must love one another or die."

The phrase *as Dr. Coco asserts* lets readers know that the ideas belong to Dr. Coco. Likewise, the quote marks and words *when he wrote* let readers know that those words belong to Auden. While Dr. Coco's words are paraphrased, Auden's words are quoted directly.

Make a list of signal words that you can use to introduce quotations, summaries, and paraphrases.

A Half Leads to a Hole

A **half-truth** is a logical fallacy in which the writer builds a claim around some facts but leaves out others. By omitting pertinent information and not telling the whole story, the writer spins the truth so that the facts support his or her argument.

Half-truths deceive the audience and damage a writer's credibility just as badly as out-and-out lies. An example of a half-truth would be telling your teacher that you couldn't complete an assignment, but neglecting to mention that you spent the night watching movies rather than writing.

Write a paragraph about a situation in which you or someone you know told a half-truth.

Physician, Heal Thy Society

Revise and edit the paragraph below. Remember to correct grammar mistakes and typos, vary sentence structure, eliminate qualifiers and intensifiers, rewrite logical fallacies, use topic and concluding sentences, and employ figurative language.

One of my heros in life has been Dr Emily Perez, a physician in my hometown. She is proof positive that the American dream comes true. She was the first person in her family to go to college but became a doctor instead of getting married when she was eighteen like her parents wanted. But she is thinking of not becoming a doctor anymore because society has grown too commercial and doctors are at the beckon call of insurance companies and money. Dr. Perez told me about a person who was sick in her office but who she couldn't treat because the company that does her insurance told her not to treat people like that. For Dr. Perez and many others in this country, the over commercialization of society is making the American dream a nightmare instead.

on't Conk Out, Reader

Using the same **sentence structure** all the time is a good way to put your readers to sleep. Avoid the dum-dum pattern of *subject verb, subject verb*. If you want readers to pay attention to your argument, you've got to keep them enthusiastic and involved.

As practice, rewrite the choppy, repetitive paragraph below into something lively and worth reading.

Lisa Rinaldi has dreams. She wants to be a pop star. She wants to make it to the top. She takes voice lessons every week. She takes dance lessons. Lisa even studies clothing design. She also goes to charm school. There, they teach her good posture and etiquette. Lisa knows none of this is enough. s MTV, BET, and American Idol to see what's hot. She goes to arties to meet producers and promoters. One day, Lisa will Her parents will be proud.

Beauty, Pulchritude

When readers pick up your essay, they want to hear your voice—not read a thesaurus. While it's a good idea to vary your word choice and use an occasional polysyllabic word, don't try to make yourself sound smarter by using a lot of big words. Plus, when you use words you don't really know, you risk misusing them. And incorrectly used words will cause your readers to lose confidence in you as a writer.

Write synonyms for each of the ten ordinary words listed below.

- Happy
- Sad
- Big
- Small
- Fat

- Tired
- Anxious
- Hungry
- Chatty
- Quiet

Born to Succeed

Think carefully about the issue presented in the following quotation from Henry David Thoreau.

"Men are born to succeed, not fail."

What is your view on the above statement? Plan and write an essay in which you develop your point of view on this issue. Support your stand with examples from your studies or experiences.

Aren't I Smart?

Rhetorical questions are questions that aren't meant to be answer̲

Here's an example:

People are fundamentally good, aren't they?

Consider opening your essay with a rhetorical question. Doing so can help prepare readers for the argument that follows.

Write three rhetorical questions—one about France, one about fashion, and one about intelligence.

nder Freewrite

Unlike brainstorming, in which writers make lists, **freewriting** means writing without stopping for a certain amount of time. When writers freewrite, they don't worry about grammar, spelling, mechanics, or word choice. Instead, they just write. The idea is to write whatever comes to mind, without worrying or censoring yourself. Freewriting is a great way to get the writing juices flowing when you're feeling stuck or blocked.

For the next five minutes, freewrite on the differences between men and women.

Birds of a Feather Don't Always Stick Together

A **package-deal fallacy** is a logical fallacy in which the writer argues that a group of things, people, events, ideas, or phenomena must stay together because they've historically or culturally always been linked. For example, when a writer claims that all Democrats believe in profligate government spending, high taxes, and gun control, that writer commits the package-deal fallacy. After all, any person, regardless of political affiliation, could believe in some, all, or none of these issues. Being a Democrat doesn't require or automatically make a person believe in historically Democratic issues.

Write **three** statements in which you commit the package-deal fallacy.

Favorite Journal

Keeping a journal, or **journaling**, can help you figure out what you want to say about a topic or issue. Journaling is different from freewriting for two reasons: first, journaling asks you to write about yourself—your thoughts, your feelings, and your experiences. Second, journaling tends to be more focused than freewriting.

A journal entry might include specific details or might consist of a complete anecdote. A piece of freewriting, in contrast, might jump from topic to topic or might be completely nonsensical to anyone but you. In general, a journal entry is more polished than a piece of freewriting.

For the next ten minutes, journal about your favorite subject in school.

She Sips Starbucks

Alliteration is the repetition of the same consonant, vowel, or sound in adjacent or nearby words. Used sparingly, alliteration can help you add emphasis to the ideas in your essay. But if your sentences sound like tongue-twisters, you'd better rewrite them for clarity.

Here's an example of an overly alliterative sentence:

> Susie sat at Starbucks, sipping a soft drink and staring at Sophie, who lapped a latte.

Here's a rewrite:

> Susie hung out at Starbucks, drinking a cola and looking at Sophie, who had a latte.

Write three sentences about your favorite outfit. Use alliteration for emphasis.

Poker Cluster

Clustering is a type of brainstorming in which writers list out and organize their ideas. To cluster, write the topic in a circle near the center of a paper. As you think of words and phrases related to the topic, write them nearby. Then draw a circle around each one. Draw arrows between the circles and the primary topic. As you think of more ideas, write them down, drawing circles around them and using arrows to link them to other ideas. The arrows should show how the ideas relate to one another.

For the next five minutes, use clustering to organize your ideas about the popularity of poker. Use *poker's popularity* as your first cluster circle.

Smart and Old

Think carefully about the issue presented in the following quotation from Greek philosopher Aristotle.

"Education is the best provision for old age."

What is your view on the above statement? Plan and write an essay in which you develop your point of view on this issue. Support your stand with examples from your studies or experiences.

Mark the Omission

Use the **ellipsis mark** (...) when you omit portions of a direct quotation. For example, the quotation "I wanted a piece of barbecued chicken" could be transformed into "I wanted ... chicken."

Ellipsis marks let your readers know that you've altered the original quotation.

Write down a few lyrics from your favorite song. Don't forget to use quotation marks. Then practice using ellipsis marks by altering and omitting some words from those lyrics.

Don't Quote Me

Put **quotation marks** around the titles of songs, poems, articles, essays, episodes of television shows, parts of books, and short stories:

- Everyone has to read "The Lady and the Tiger" in high school.

- For fun, my parents sit in our living room and listen to "Bridge Over Troubled Water" on repeat.

To memorize the rules governing the use of quotation marks, write a paragraph about your favorite musician or band. Don't forget to mention your favorite songs.

Call Me

Oversimplification is a logical fallacy in which a writer oversimplifies the connections between two phenomena or events. For example:

> We need to continue testing medicine on animals. If we stop, we'll never again find another cure for a disease.

This writer overstates the connections between animal testing and the discovery of medical cures.

Write a paragraph in which you oversimplify the relationship between cell phone use and popularity.

To Be or Not to Be

Quotations longer than four lines do not get quote marks. Instead, they begin on a new line, indented ten spaces from the margin. This technique is referred to as block quoting. A citation is usually inserted at the end of the quotation. Observe:

> Of all Hamlet's soliloquies, the "To Be or Not to Be" monologue is perhaps the most famous. It begins:
>> To be, or not to be, that is the question:
>> Whether 'tis nobler in the mind to suffer
>> The slings and arrows of outrageous fortune, or to take arms against a sea of troubles
>> And by opposing end them. To die—to sleep,
>> No more (III.i.56–61)

Choose four or more lines from your favorite song or poem. Write a short paragraph that discusses them in detail and use block quoting to introduce and cite the lines.

Out of Cite

Direct quotations, summaries, and paraphrases must be acknowledged, or **cited**. Citations let readers know that you've done your research and where they can go to get more information, should they want to read more about the ideas you've cited.

There are two ways to style in-text citations. One way is to include the name of the author within the body of your sentence and to cite the page number in parentheses:

George Orwell describes a terrifying dystopia in 1984, a land in which "Big Brother Is Watching You" (5).

The second citation style consists of inserting the name of the author in parentheses, along with the page number:

The handball team needs "guts, luck, and skill" to win the world championship (Ziegler 178).

Write a short paragraph about a book you've been reading. Include a mix of correctly cited quotes, paraphrases, and summaries.

Cell Phones Cited

Whenever you consult outside sources for an essay, you must list those sources on what's called a **works cited page** or **bibliography**. Always start your works cited page on a separate page, following the last page of your essay. Title it "Works Cited".

Alphabetize your sources, and style them as follows:

- For books: Last name, First name. Title of Book. City of Publication: Name of Publisher, Date of Publication.

  de Bottain, Alain. How Proust Can Change Your Life. New York: Vintage, 1997.
- For magazine or journal articles: Last name, First name. "Title of Article in Quote Marks." Name of Magazine or Journal Volume Number. Issue Number (Date of Publication): Page Numbers.

  Cooper, Imelda. "How to Understand Your Cat." Fancy Pet 32.5 (2005): 93–99.
- For websites: Last name, First name. Title of Site. Date of last update. Name of Organization Associated with Site (if any). Date of Access. URL in angle brackets.

  Affalo, Peter. All About Plants. March 2004. United Botanists. 31 August 2005. <http://www.unitedbotanists.com/allaboutplants>.

Imagine you're writing an essay on cell phones. Make up five reliable sources and list them on a works cited page.

Hail to the Chief

General outlines help you organize your thoughts and arrange the elements of your argument. Use the outline form below to plan out an argumentative essay about why you'd make a good president.

Thesis statement: _____

Main point of first body paragraph: _____

Supporting details: _____

Main point of second body paragraph: _____

Supporting details: _____

Main point of third body paragraph: _____

Supporting details: _____

Notes for conclusion: _____

Cinematic Pros and Cons

Listing pros and cons is another great way to brainstorm. Making a list of all of the advantages and disadvantages of an issue can help you determine which side you're on—whether you're pro or con.

Create and fill in a pro-and-con chart for the following statement: Students should be required to study film, not literature, in high school.

Ferraris and Hybrids

Unlike brainstorming, in which writers make lists, **freewriting** means writing without stopping for a certain amount of time. When writers freewrite, they don't worry about grammar, spelling, mechanics, or word choice. Instead, they just write. The idea is to write whatever comes to mind, without worrying or censoring yourself. Freewriting is a great way to get the writing juices flowing when you're feeling stuck or blocked.

For the next five minutes, freewrite on the topic of cars.

Don't Smoke and Drive

Wordy sentences go on and on but don't seem to say much. All too often, long, complicated sentences end up confusing readers and muddling your argument.

As a brain-stretching exercise, make the sentence below as long as possible. Use a ton of adjectives, employ the passive voice and present progressive (-*ing* verbs), and string together clause after clause with commas.

Legislators have proposed a measure to ban smoking while driving.

An Expensive Journal

Keeping a journal, or **journaling**, can help you figure out what you want to say about a topic or issue. Journaling is different from freewriting for two reasons: first, journaling asks you to write about yourself—your thoughts, your feelings, and your experiences. Second, journaling tends to be more focused than freewriting.

A journal entry might include specific details or might consist of a complete anecdote. A piece of freewriting, in contrast, might jump from topic to topic or might be completely nonsensical to anyone but you. In general, a journal entry is more polished than a piece of freewriting.

For the next ten minutes, journal about your attitude toward money.

Misery, Defined

Think carefully about the issue presented in the following quotation from American poet Wallace Stevens.

> "That's what misery is,
> Nothing to have at heart.
> It is to have or nothing."

What is your view on the above statement? Plan and write an essay in which you develop your point of view on this issue. Support your stand with examples from your studies or experiences.

iers and Intensifiers

qualifiers and **intensifiers** will make your writing sound clear and strong, while using them will make your writing sound padded and pointless. Qualifiers include *to be completely honest, to tell you the truth,* and *in my humble opinion.* Intensifiers include *absolutely, really,* and *quite.*

Rewrite the following sentences, deleting all qualifiers and intensifiers:

- In my humble opinion, Jenna is absolutely the best choice for class president.
- It's absolutely apparent that this administration's approach to security is completely incompetent.
- I really am quite certain that the entire house is totally and even more than totally safe from intruders.
- To be candid with you, Alice, we are completely thrilled, honestly and truly, that you are joining the family.

Five Paragraphs on Malls

Most high school essays rely on the **five-paragraph model** of organization. model has an **introductory paragraph** that starts generally and ends with your main claim or thesis statement; three **body paragraphs**, each of which explains a separate supporting idea, and each of which gives lots of evidence and analysis; and a **concluding paragraph** that sums up your claims and argument.

Make an outline for a five-paragraph essay in response to the following claim: Shopping malls and mall culture are destroying America.

ove Semicolons; Really, I Do

DAILY SPARK

Semicolons can be used instead of a period or a conjunction to join two closely connected independent clauses.

Here's an example of how a semicolon can be used instead of a period:

- Joey hates going to the movies. Indeed, she cannot stand the smell of popcorn.
- Joey hates going to the movies; indeed, she cannot stand the smell of popcorn.

Here's an example of how a semicolon can be used instead of a conjunction, such as *but, or, nor, for, because,* and *yet*:

- Rhoda longed to decorate the apartment in various aquamarine hues, because the blue colors reminded her of marine biology, her major in college.
- Rhoda longed to decorate the apartment in various aquamarine hues; the blue colors reminded her of marine biology, her major in college.

Write four sentences—two that use a semicolon in place of a period and two that use a semicolon in place of a conjunction.

Fragmentary Grammar

A complete sentence contains a subject and a correctly conjugated verb. A **sentence fragment** contains either a subject or a verb—but not both. Here's a sentence fragment that lacks a verb:

> The one movie you've been waiting for, from the classic novel of adventure and suspense.

You might correct it by writing: The one movie you've been waiting for, from the classic novel of adventure and suspense, hits theaters this July.

Here's a fragment missing the subject:

> Woke up this morning, found corn chips in my bed.

You might correct it by writing: I woke up this morning and found corn chips in my bed.

Create four sentence fragments of your own—one about fast food, one about cats, one about cars, and one about forest fires. Then correct them by turning the fragments into complete sentences.

Thoughtful Activism

Think carefully about the issue presented in the following quotation from American anthropologist Margaret Mead.

"Never doubt that a small group of thoughtful committed citizens can change the world. Indeed, it is the only thing that ever has."

What is your view on the above statement? Plan and write an essay in which you develop your point of view on this issue. Support your stand with examples from your studies or experiences.

Welcome to My Paragraph

Good writers use **topic sentences** to structure their paragraphs and organize their arguments. A topic sentence tells your readers what the paragraph is about and shows them how that paragraph links to your main argument. Topic sentences say, Here's what I plan to discuss and here's why I'm discussing it.

For practice, take a look at the topic sentences below. Based on the topic sentences, what do you think the rest of the paragraph might say? Pick one sentence and jot down some notes about what you think the subsequent paragraph might say.

- Holden Caulfied, the narrator of *The Catcher in the Rye*, is neither pathological nor insane. Instead, he is simply just another troubled teen struggling to enter adulthood.
- Although expensive, this new surgical technique has the potential to revolutionize medicine.
- Mark Twain's controversial use of dialect increases the overall realism and vividness of *Huckleberry Finn*.

119

The Uses of Beauty

Think carefully about the issue presented in the following quotation from English critic John Ruskin.

> "The most beautiful things in the world are the most useless, peacocks and lilies, for instance."

What is your view on the above statement? Plan and write an essay in which you develop your point of view on this issue. Support your stand with examples from your studies or experiences.

Winston Smiths of the World, Unite!

Revise and edit the paragraph below. Remember to correct grammar mistakes and typos, vary sentence structure, eliminate qualifiers and intensifiers, rewrite logical fallacies, use topic and concluding sentences, and employ figurative language.

George Orwell's novel 1984, though it did not come true when he said it would, is a powerful indictment of contemporary society. From mall security cameras to cell phone tracking devices to computer spyware, our world resembles the world that Orwell was terrified of. That's why we need more Winston Smiths, people are unwilling to stay afrade and fight the system. Therefore its only logical that instead of reading 1984 as just a novel we should be reading it as a call to arms. Teachers should be required to teach how we can fight this overwhelming government control. The government controls too much of our daily lives and therefore school should force students to develop the tools to fight back like Winston Smith. I—I mean we are not going to take it anymore.

This Quote Shows....

If you want to persuade readers of something, you need to give them reasons, evidence, and explanations. You need to take readers by the hand and guide them through your argument. Each piece of evidence needs at least one **analysis sentence**. This sentence should explain why your evidence supports your argument.

Brainstorm a list of ten words that you might include in analysis sentences.

Cheerfully, Nicely

Adverbs modify adjectives, verbs, and other adverbs. Adverbs also help make your writing colorful and snazzy. See how many adverbs you can come up with to modify the nouns in the sentence below. Try to include at least twenty adverbs per blank.

Sandra _____ opened the front door and _____ walked into the living room.

Go Team

As a brain-stretching exercise, write a paragraph in support of the claim below. Cite fantastical sources, give fake statistics, quote imaginary people, and use only made-up evidence.

Homecoming festivities, including a fall dance, pep rally, and football game, help student morale and lead to higher test scores.

Correct Contractions

Think fast: what are the contractions of *could have*, *should have*, and *would have*?

The word *have* always contracts to an apostrophe plus *ve*, never *of* or *a*: I would've if I could've, and I know I should've.

To help you memorize this rule, write a paragraph in which you tell the story of someone who should have, could have, or would have done something.

No Offense

Always strive to keep your writing neutral and fair. Avoid any apparent bias concerning gender, race, age, or ethnicity. Remember: your readers won't favor your argument or listen to your ideas if they feel offended or excluded. Rather than write *policeman*, try *police officer*. Instead of *waiter*, say *server*.

Rewrite the following job titles, using gender-neutral and bias-free language:

- Fireman
- Stewardess
- Actress
- Mailwoman
- Poetess
- Salesman

Outrageous or Prim?

Grammar is the substance of good writing, whereas **style** is the pizzazz of good writing. We often say that a fashionable person has a great sense of style; this compliment holds true for great writing as well. In fact, every great writer has a certain style that transcends whatever he or she is writing about. Style lets us distinguish between a sentence written by Edgar Allan Poe and a sentence written by J. D. Salinger.

Think of an outrageous person whose style you admire. Then write a paragraph about this person, using an equally outrageous literary style. For instance, a paragraph about Lenny Kravitz might have a lot of exclamation points and sentences fragments, while a paragraph about Nicole Kidman might be very proper and might follow all of the rules of grammar.

Speaking Freely

Revise and edit the paragraph below. Remember to correct grammar mistakes and typos, vary sentence structure, eliminate qualifiers and intensifiers, rewrite logical fallacies, use topic and concluding sentences, and employ figurative language.

Free speech is the most important value their is, more important than any other value in our society. If the U.S.A. didn't have free speech, we wouldn't be able to criticize the government when it was doing bad and people wouldn't be able to speak freely. Or be themselves. It seems like everywhere you look though free speech is not being protected. Its not protected in many of America's homes where people can be punished severely for speaking out of line. It's not protected in schools, where no profanity is allowed. It's not protected in libraries where books are banned, like in one school in the North East. Freedom isn't free but free speech is priceless. We must learn to defend our freedoms or we will pay the price with our freedoms.

In Conclusion

Every essay needs a **conclusion**. The final paragraph is your chance to use language, imagery, and ideas to leave a lasting impression on your readers. But your conclusion should do more than simply restate your argument. Instead, use your conclusion to:

- Cite a quotation and interpret that quotation within the context of your argument.
- Apply your argument to a related topic.
- Discuss how your idea reaches beyond the scope of the topic or matters in some larger context.
- Ask a question of your readers, or urge them to take action.

Choose one of the techniques listed above. Then write a concluding paragraph for **an essay arguing** about what makes a good teacher.

...re You a Happy Youth?

Think carefully about the issue presented in the following quotation from English writer W. Somerset Maugham.

"It is an illusion that youth is happy, an illusion of those who have lost it."

What is your view on the above statement? Plan and write an essay in which you develop your point of view on this issue. Support your stand with examples from your studies or experiences.

Opposites Attract

Antithesis is a special effect in language that jazzes up your writing. In antithesis, a writer uses parallel structures to highlight opposites or contrasting ideas, usually in the same sentence. For example:

It's one small step for man, one giant leap for mankind.

Write three examples of antithesis. If you get stuck, try thinking of pairs of opposites (*life, death; good, evil*) around which you can then build your sentences.

Creative Destruction

Think carefully about the issue presented in the following quotation from Pablo Picasso.

"Every act of creation is first an act of destruction."

What is your view on the above statement? Plan and write an essay in which you develop your point of view on this issue. Support your stand with examples from your studies or experiences.

The Argumentative Wrap-Up

Write a conclusion for an essay that argues that _____
[fill in the blank with a book of your choice] should be required reading for
all high school students in the United States.

et Diversity Be Different!

Revise and edit the paragraph below. Remember to correct grammar mistakes and typos, vary sentence structure, eliminate qualifiers and intensifiers, rewrite logical fallacies, use topic and concluding sentences, and employ figurative language.

Diversity is what makes the world turn. From the smallest flower bed to the largest jungle diversity is the most important characteristic of life on this Earth. Many people however try to fit in when they should be focusing on developing themsevles as individuals. Wearing the coolest clothes or having the most songs on your iPod is not a way to become individualized. However this is what many people including my peers care about the most. But parent's and teachers are just as bad and don't teach the kids inviduality. Instead they punish kids who act differently like by wearing more goth clothes or dying their hair a strange color. We should learn instead to appreciate diversity in all its different forms.

I Like Lists

Parallelism requires that the different parts of a sentence start, continue, and end in the same way. Here's a sentence that has serious problems with parallelism:

> In the summer, I like eating lobster, to go swimming, and volleyball.

In a series or list, all the items must follow the same pattern—that is, if the first item is a verb, then all of the subsequent items must also be verbs. If the first item uses the *–ing* ending, then all of the subsequent items must also end in *–ing*. Here are two correct versions of the sentence above:

- In the summer, I like to eat lobster, go swimming, and play volleyball.
- In the summer, I like eating lobster, going swimming, and playing volleyball.

Fix the parallelism problems in the sentences below:

- A good sense of fashion requires corduroy trousers, a beaded necklace, and to buy six pairs of tube socks.
- On Saturday, Dolores rode the rollercoaster, watched a movie, and corn on the cob.
- Coco brought seven doughnuts, sixteen cupcakes, and she made a ham plus her famous vanilla milkshake.

Keep Art Free

An **allusion** is a reference to a familiar person, place, or thing. Allusions are particularly common in poetry and other types of creative writing but also work well in argumentative essays. The best allusions achieve their effect by invoking important or memorable ideas, things, phenomena, people, or works of art. Here's an example of an allusive opening to an essay about artistic freedom:

> Imagine a world like that of *Fahrenheit 451*. What if we had no books or art? What if our government burned every copy of *The Adventures of Huckleberry Finn* because some people say it is racist and others say it encourages bad behavior? What if Michelangelo's *David* were hacked to ruins because it made young girls think impure thoughts?

Think of an issue about which you feel strongly. Then come up with at least three allusions you could make in an essay about that issue.

Padding Is for Chairs

Don't pad your paragraphs. Every sentence of every paragraph in your essay must serve a purpose and must contribute to the argument. To make sure that every sentence serves a purpose, ask yourself **why have I included this?** after each sentence. If you can't answer honestly, rewrite or delete the sentence.

Write a short paragraph in which you argue that every American should own a pet. Make sure that every sentence passes the **why?** test.

A Star Is Born

Think carefully about the issue presented in the following quotation from German philosopher Friedrich Nietzsche.

> "One must still have chaos in oneself to be able to give birth to a dancing star."

What is your view on the above statement? Plan and write an essay in which you develop your point of view on this issue. Support your stand with examples from your studies or experiences.

Hungry for an Essay

An **analogy** compares an unfamiliar idea to a familiar one. Analogies are especially helpful when you need to explain a difficult or complex idea. For example, some writing teachers use a hamburger as a way of explaining the five-paragraph essay: the two buns are the introductory and concluding paragraphs, while the lettuce, tomato, and patty are the body paragraphs. This explanation makes a hamburger *analogous* to the five-paragraph essay.

Create an analogy for each of the topics listed below:

- The relationship between you and one member of your family
- Your struggles with your worst school subject or sport
- A political crisis in the headlines
- The most important day of the school year

Sí, Oui, Lo, Nein

Clustering is a type of brainstorming in which writers list and organize their ideas. To cluster, write the topic in a circle near the center of a piece of paper. As you think of words and phrases related to the topic, write them nearby. Then draw a circle around each one. Draw arrows between the circles and the primary topic. As you think of more ideas, write them down, drawing circles around them and using arrows to link them to other ideas. The arrows should show how the ideas relate to one another.

Spend the next five minutes using clustering to organize your ideas about foreign language requirements. Should students be required to learn a foreign language before graduating from high school? Use your answer to this question as your first cluster circle.

Agree with Me

The subject of a sentence must always agree in number with the verb of the sentence. In other words, a singular subject always goes with a singular verb, and a plural subject always takes a plural verb.

Sometimes, though, it can be difficult to determine whether a subject is singular or plural, especially in the following cases:

- **Compound subjects**: the dog and the cat sat, fish and chips taste good, Harry and Sally walk
- **Indefinite pronouns**: everybody hurts, nobody tries, both like beans, few fail
- **Collective nouns**: the committee agrees, the family understands

Write three sentences in which the subjects and verbs agree—one that has a compound subject, one that uses an indefinite pronoun, and one that contains a collective noun.

Lissome, Chunky, Bucolic

Adjectives jazz up writing by providing vivid descriptions. See how many adjectives you can come up with to modify the nouns in the sentence below. Try to include at least twenty adjectives per blank. As you're thinking of adjectives, pay attention to how different descriptors will change the meaning of the sentence.

The _____ man walked his _____ dog through the _____ park.

Every Cloud and Other Fish

When writing, do whatever you can to avoid **clichés**. Clichés are overused comparisons, adages, and expressions. Here are a few examples of phrases and expressions to avoid *like the plague*:

- Kick the bucket
- Between a rock and a hard place
- Every cloud has a silver lining
- Wet blanket
- There are other fish in the sea

List five clichés. Then use new words and fresh language to rewrite each phrase or expression.

The Palace of Wisdom

Think carefully about the issue presented in the following quotation from English poet William Blake.

"The road of excess leads to the palace of wisdom."

What is your view on the above statement? Plan and write an essay in which you develop your point of view on this issue. Support your stand with examples from your studies or experiences.

I'll Drink to That

Revise and edit the paragraph below. Remember to correct grammar mistakes a
typos, vary sentence structure, eliminate qualifiers and intensifiers, rewrite logical
fallacies, use topic and concluding sentences, and employ figurative language.

Consider this: a person, let's call him Joe, can be put in the military and go
to another country and die for his country but yet Joe can't come back and
buy alcohol. Is this communist Russia, you ask? No! It's the good old U.S. of
A., where the drinking age is 21 but the age to serve in the military is only
18! How can it be that Joe can be responsible enough to protect America's
bars and restaurants but not responsible enough to drink in them or buy
alchol at the convenience store. They say that people who are under 21
are more likely to drink and drive and that's the reason; but drinking and
driving is common at any age. Thus we can see that the age to buy alcohol
should be lowered or else we will risk a revolution at the hands of our
young soldiers.

s Stuff

...st **vague writing**. They don't understand it, and they begin to

...t the writer is trying to put something over on them. Keep readers on

...side by:

- Choosing clear and specific words when you write
- Focusing on using strong, vivid words and expressions
- Avoiding poorly defined terms and euphemisms, such as *family values* or *wonderfully diverse population*
- Never, ever using clichés

Write an advertisement for a miracle cure-all product. Be as vague as possible about what the elixir actually cures. Switch papers with a classmate and see if you can guess what your classmate's advertising.

Justify Your Movie Love

Formal outlines are more complicated than rough outlines. Writers use formal outlines to figure out where every idea and supporting detail will go in each paragraph. A formal outline identifies headings, subheadings, and details, using a combination of Roman numbers, Arabic numbers, and letters.

Here's how it works:

Start with your topic or thesis.
I. Large Roman numerals present the topic sentence.
   A. Uppercase letters present subtopics.
      1. Arabic numerals provide evidence.
         a. Lowercase letters explain evidence and show how evidence connects to the paragraph's main claim.
            i. Lowercase Roman numerals provide further details about the evidence.

Pick one aspect of a recent movie that you really loved, such as the dialogue, setting, plot, pacing, or lead actor. Then write a formal outline in which you make an argument about why everyone should see this movie, taking your evidence and ideas from the one aspect you really loved.

The Logic of Grilled Cheese

Writing good outlines requires you to think logically about arguments. To get some practice thinking and writing logically, write a rough outline in which you explain step-by-step how to make a grilled-cheese sandwich.

American Cluster

Clustering is a type of brainstorming in which writers list out and organize their ideas. To cluster, write the topic in a circle near the center of a piece of paper. As you think of words and phrases related to the topic, write them nearby. Then draw a circle around each one. Draw arrows between the circles and the primary topic. As you think of more ideas, write them down, drawing circles around them and using arrows to link them to other ideas. The arrows should show how the ideas relate to one another.

Spend the next five minutes using clustering to organize your ideas about what it means to be "American." Use *American* as your first cluster circle.

Put It in Reverse

After you have a first draft of an essay, try making a **reverse outline**. In a reverse outline, you list out what you've actually written in each paragraph. Unlike formal or rough outlines, which help you plan your argument before you begin writing, reverse outlines help you see how you've organized your argument *after* you've begun writing.

To get some practice doing reverse outlines, read a short magazine article. Using complete sentences, summarize each of the article's main points and pieces of evidence using a reverse outline.

Co-ed Journal

Keeping a journal, or **journaling**, can help you figure out what you want to say about a topic or issue. Journaling is different from freewriting for two reasons: first, journaling asks you to write about yourself—your thoughts, your feelings, and your experiences. Second, journaling tends to be more focused than freewriting.

A journal entry might include specific details or might consist of a complete anecdote. A piece of freewriting, in contrast, might jump from topic to topic or might be completely nonsensical to anyone but you. In general, a journal entry is more polished than a piece of freewriting.

For the next ten minutes, journal about the advantages and disadvantages of high school co-education.

Does Albert Speak the Truth?

Think carefully about the issue presented in the following quotation from Albert Einstein.

"Unthinking respect for authority is the greatest enemy of truth."

What is your view on the above statement? Plan and write an essay in which you develop your point of view on this issue. Support your stand with examples from your studies or experiences.

Just the Facts, Ma'am

In critical writing, a **claim** is the main point you're trying to assert or argue. There are four types of claims:

- A **claim of fact** states something that can be proven to be true or untrue: Extraterrestrial life exists.
- A **claim of value** states that something has or lacks worth: Animation is as important an art form as painting.
- A **claim of policy or solution** states an opinion about whether something ought to be done: All seniors should be given the opportunity to graduate in January.
- A **claim of cause and effect** makes inferences about the relationship between two or more actions or occurrences: Listening to hip-hop leads to higher SAT scores.

Write five claims of fact.

Standardized Freewrite

Unlike brainstorming, in which writers make lists, **freewriting** means writing without stopping for a certain amount of time. When writers freewrite, they don't worry about grammar, spelling, mechanics, or word choice. Instead, they just write. The idea is to write whatever comes to mind, without worrying or censoring yourself. Freewriting is a great way to get the writing juices flowing when you're feeling stuck or blocked.

Take the next five minutes to freewrite on the topic of the SAT or the ACT.

Great Books Brainstorm

Brainstorming means listing all of the ideas related to a topic. When writers brainstorm, they don't worry about whether the ideas are plausible or even interesting. Instead, they just list everything they can possibly think of that might be relevant.

When brainstorming, write down everything that comes to mind, even if it seems silly or stupid. You never know which ideas might actually work.

Imagine you've been charged with coming up with a list of must-read, great books for your high school English class. What would be on your list? Don't worry about defending your choices—just list them.

Separate, Yet Together

In **compound sentences**, two independent clauses are joined by a **conjunction**, such as *and*, *but*, *so*, *or*, *nor*, or *for*. A comma comes immediately before the conjunction.

For instance:

Pablo had hoped for chicken, yet his uncle insisted on cooking salmon.

Write five compound sentences. Place a comma before the conjunction in each one.

Evaluate This!

In an **evaluation essay**, the writer makes judgments about a topic, trend, pheno-menon, person, situation, or idea. These essays try to persuade the readers of a particular judgment or evaluation. Examples of evaluation essays include movie and book reviews.

Write a short review of the last book you read.

Shall I Compare Thee....

In a **compare-and-contrast essay**, writers compare at least two topics in order to persuade their readers and to argue a particular position. When writing a compare-and-contrast essay, remember that your topics must be somehow related and thus worthy of comparison. For instance, you might compare and contrast planes and trains to come to some conclusions about transportation, but you wouldn't want to try to compare painting and vanilla ice cream.

Imagine that you have to write an argumentative essay on the topic of extracurricular activities. You must decide whether to require extracurricular activities of all students at your high school. List at least six topics or ideas that you might consider comparing and contrasting as you make your argument.

A Symbolic Analysis

An **analytical essay** requires you to closely read parts of a work in order to make an argument about the text as a whole. To write this type of essay, you'll need to:

- Choose a few key paragraphs or sections of a written work on which to focus your analysis.
- Examine these key paragraphs for interesting patterns or features. Look for metaphors, similes, comparisons, word choice, tone, organization, and character development.
- Use the patterns or features to draw conclusions about the author's style or rhetoric; the text's relationship to a specific period in history or type of culture; or the meaning of a repeated theme, symbol or motif.

Examples of analytical essays include an argument about the important symbols in a text, such as the whale in *Moby-Dick* or the doppelgangers in *Mrs. Dalloway*.

To get a feel for analytical writing, think of a recurring symbol in the last novel you read, or consider the hunting hat in *The Catcher in the Rye* or Big Brother in *1984*. Then write a paragraph in which you begin to make an argument about this symbol's significance to the text as a whole.

Hamlet's Great

For practice, revise and edit the introductory paragraph below. Remember to correct grammar mistakes and typos, vary sentence structure, eliminate qualifiers and intensifiers, rewrite logical fallacies, use topic and concluding sentences, and employ figurative language.

Its hard to say how great *Hamlet* is. Is it the greatest English literature piece? Probably. Greatness though is difficult to define, however *Hamlet*'s greatness is that we still read it today. One of the reasons why I can tell that *Hamlet* is a great piece of literature is that I read it over and ovel all the time and still find that it speaks to me and our current situation in the modern world. The modern world is complex. And so is Hamlet. So we can tell that Shakespeare wrote Hamlet as a metaphor of our human condition in the modern world. Shakespeare was a head of his time. Therefore *Hamlet* is the greatest work of literature.

Lovingly Defined

A **definition essay** requires you to make an argument by definition. For example, a definition essay might define a political or philosophical concept, such as racism or knowledge.

In this type of essay, you persuade readers to accept your definition of the topic or concept. These essays move beyond dictionary definitions to thoughtful, interesting analyses that argue claims and explain evidence.

When writing a definition essay, you might start with a dictionary definition of the concept, but then you'll also want to discuss how the meaning has changed over time and what factors might influence the meaning.

Write a paragraph in which you begin to define love.

Ramble On, Brother

A rambling sentence seems to go on and on, often because of the overuse of the word *and*. Observe:

Rambling: The saleswoman explained to us the benefits of selecting her brand and discussed with us its many original features and extra options and we thought it seemed like a better deal than our current cell phone plan because her plan came with two free lines.

Corrected: The saleswoman went over her company's cell phone plan with us, discussing its benefits. She told us about its many original features and extra options. We thought it seemed like a better deal than our current plan.

Write a paragraph in which you ramble on and on about your favorite type of technology for at least four sentences. Then correct your paragraph by inserting punctuation and rewriting sentences for clarity.

Colons: Cool

Colons can do a couple of things within sentences, such as:

- Emphasize a part of a sentence: I have one goal for myself: to win the hot dog–eating contest.

- Introduce a list: Bruce, go to the bookstore and buy the following: three romance novels, six mystery novels, two books on Latin American economic policy, and one cookbook.

- Provide a formal introduction to a sentence, question, or quotation: William Blake is credited with this observation: "It is easier to forgive an enemy than to forgive a friend."

Come up with three sentences—one that uses a colon to emphasize, one that uses a colon to introduce a list, and one that gives a formal introduction.

All the World's a Stage

Like similes, **metaphors** compare two things. Unlike similes, metaphors do not use the words *like* or *as*. Here's an example from Shakespeare's *As You Like It*:

> All the world's a stage,
> And all the men and women merely players
> They have their exits and their entrances (II.vii.142–144)

Write a metaphor for each of the following topics:

- Manual labor
- Driving
- Politics
- Shopping or consumer culture
- High school

In Spring, Rain Falls

As you write, try to vary your **sentence structure**. Use a combination of long and short sentences. Avoid space wasters like *I believe* and *I think*. Don't begin sentences with *It is* or *There are*. Mix up your clauses: sometimes you should put the most important information first, and sometimes you should put it last.

Write a five-sentence paragraph about a season or type of weather. Remember to vary your sentence structure.

Tell Me a Story

Writers use **narrative essays** to dramatize events and tell stories. Although narrative essays share some features with short stories, including plots, characters, and dialogues, narrative essays are usually nonfiction, or factual, and short stories are usually fictional, or completely made up.

Narrative essays usually have a point to make or a point of view to expose. Examples of narrative essays include a description of your first day of school that concludes by advocating for an education trend, or the story of how your parents met that ends by supporting the idea of love at first sight.

Write an anecdote, or story, from your own life to illustrate one of the following ideas:

- Maturity
- Creativity
- a unique world view

Your Family, Informally and Formally

There's a difference between informal English, or the way you speak with your friends, and formal English, or the way you write academic essays. Informal English is full of clichés, colloquialisms, slang, regional dialects, and contractions, and it loosely follows the rules of grammar. Formal English is full of proper grammar and vocabulary and does not use colloquialisms, slang, or regional dialects. Also, formal English always obeys the rules of grammar.

Here's an example of a sentence written in informal English and formal English:

Informal: Yo, like, my hella-smart girl Bev got brain and no wanna channel-surf 24-7.

Formal: My very smart friend Beverly does not want to watch television all the time.

Write five sentences in informal English about your family. Then translate those sentences into formal English.

Computers Good, Field Hockey Bad

Revise and edit the paragraph below. Remember to correct grammar mistakes and typos, vary sentence structure, eliminate qualifiers and intensifiers, rewrite logical fallacies, use topic and concluding sentences, and employ figurative language.

The internet is the global communications system. It connects the entire world onto blogs websites, news informational sources and other important information. Yet many of the people especially young people in schools and high schools around the country don't even have there own computers yet at school. Many schools use their investment dollars poorly and don't have enought computers to supply all of internet needs of today's modern teenagers and high school students. Instead of spending so much money on athletics and art programs that no one even cares about like the school musical or girls field hockey, the schools should spend more money on the internet and computer needs of its students.

Substandardized Tests

Revise and edit the paragraph below. Remember to correct grammar mistakes and typos, vary sentence structure, eliminate qualifiers and intensifiers, rewrite logical fallacies, use topic and concluding sentences, and employ figurative language.

Standardized testing or the so-called SAT and ACT is widely practiced. Tens of millions of students every year are subjected to these tests to measure their supposed ability levels. These tests often determine who goes into what college, like if you will get into the Ivy League or not. But did you know that these tests don't really predict how students will do in college? Instead they measure ability levels, but not ability to perform in the classroom. Since we know that students ability and their grades are nearly always the same (the smartest student will almost always get all A's), this means that the tests are flawed because their not predicting student's grades accurately. Therefore the tests should be gotten rid of for changed to make them predict how well students will do once they get into the college of their choice.

She Accepts the Effects

Do you know the difference between these commonly confused words? To demonstrate your understanding, write a sentence for each of the word groups below:

- Accept, except
- Affect, effect
- Fewer, less
- Imply, infer
- It's, its
- There, their, they're

Janet Doesn't Do Donuts

A **comma splice** consists of two independent clauses joined together by a comma. For instance, *The valet carried the bags, the maid cleaned the room* is a comma splice.

There are a few ways to correct a comma splice:

- Replace the comma with a period: The valet carried the bags. The maid cleaned the room.
- Separate the independent clauses by adding a conjunction (*and*, *but*, *or*, *nor*, *for*, *yet*, *so*) after the comma: The valet carried the bags, and the maid cleaned the room.
- Replace the comma with a semicolon: The valet carried the bags; the maid cleaned the room.

Correct the following comma splices:

- Janet likes bagels, she won't want a donut for breakfast.
- Papandayan, in Java, Indonesia, and Colima, in Jalisco, Mexico, are my favorite volcanoes, they could blow at any time.
- Samson volunteered at the cat shelter every Monday night, Garrett had to eat dinner by himself.
- Chicken salad is a poor choice for such a sultry afternoon, it will spoil.

171

Run, Sentence, Run

A **run-on sentence** consists of two independent clauses joined together without punctuation. For instance, *They fell in love so fast they got married six days after they met on the cruise to Tunisia* is a run-on sentence.

There are a few ways to correct a run-on sentence:

- Insert a period between the two independent clauses: They fell in love so fast. They got married six days after they met on the cruise to Tunisia.
- Separate the independent clauses by adding a conjunction (*and*, *but*, *or*, *nor*, *for*, *yet*, *so*) and a comma: They fell in love so fast, so they got married six days after they met on the cruise to Tunisia.
- Insert a semicolon between the two independent clauses: They fell in love so fast; they got married six days after they met on the cruise to Tunisia.

Write a paragraph about how your parents or grandparents met, but don't use any punctuation. Then fix the run-on paragraph by adding punctuation and conjunctions where appropriate.

A Beautiful Cluster

Clustering is a type of brainstorming in which writers list and organize their ideas. To cluster, write the topic in a circle near the center of a piece of paper. As you think of words and phrases related to the topic, write them nearby. Then draw a circle around each one. Draw arrows between the circles and the primary topic. As you think of more ideas, write them down, drawing circles around them and using arrows to link them to other ideas. The arrows should show how the ideas relate to one another.

Spend the next five minutes using clustering to organize your ideas about beauty. Use *beauty* as your first cluster circle.

Cooking Like Fire

Similes compare unlike things by using the words *like* or *as*:

> I wandered lonely as a cloud, while he sat like a log.

Write a paragraph about cooking. Include at least five similes.

Ideas Are Like Sausages

If you want readers to follow your argument, you need to link your ideas together. One way to do this is to use **transition words**. These words show your readers how your ideas fit together and make your writing easier to read. Here are some commonly used transition words:

- To show comparison: *also, as, in the same way, like, likewise, similarly*
- To show contrast: *although, but, however, on the other hand, still, yet*
- To add information: *additionally, along with, also, and, another, as well, for instance, for example, in addition, likewise, moreover*
- To make ideas clearer: *for instance, in other words, that is*

Write a paragraph about a controversial school rule. Use transitions to link your ideas together.

Talk Their Talk

Jargon is the specialized vocabulary used by members of a profession, trade, or group.

Editors talk about *stetting* and *proofing*, while lawyers file *brief*s, professors *adjunct*, and computer techs use *DSB cables* and *dongles*. While some jargon can show your readers that you speak their language and understand them, too much jargon clogs up argumentative writing.

Think about a career or job that interests you. Then write a short paragraph about the career or job, incorporating its jargon into your writing.

An Argumentative Argument

An **argumentative essay** requires you to argue a position through reasoning and evidence. This type of writing asks that you make an argument, which is why argumentative essays are also called **persuasive essays**. You are trying to convince or persuade your readers of something. Argumentative essays have two main components: **claims** and **evidence**. An argumentative essay might urge readers to begin using fuel-efficient cars.

For the next five minutes, brainstorm three pieces of evidence you might use to persuade your readers to eat candy for breakfast.

I'm Talking to You

Writing is a **conversation** between the writer and the reader. As you write, remember to keep your reader in mind. Always consider the questions your reader might have or might want to ask you and try to put your answers into your essay.

To get some practice thinking about writing as a conversation, write out a conversation between you and a friend, classmate, or family member. During this conversation, try to convince the other person that studying abroad should be a requirement for all American high school students.

A Pencil, a Mohawk, a Sweatshirt

Details keep your readers involved in your writing. Adjectives, adverbs, and descriptions help readers use their imaginations, which further links your readers to your argument. No matter what type of essay you're writing, remember to use specific, evocative details.

Write a paragraph in which you describe something right in front of you—a classmate, a bulletin board, a book, or a shoe. Make the description as evocative as possible by using a lot of adverbs and adjectives.

I Love <u>Wedding Crashers</u>

Italicize or <u>underline</u> the names of books, plays, movies, long poems, musical compositions, magazines, newspapers, websites, television shows, paintings, and sculptures:

- The *New York Times* article discussed the Roman Polanski remake of *Oliver Twist*.

- Do you know <u>The Waste Land</u>?

- Have you seen *The Office*? It's hilarious, especially the "Christmas Special" episode.

To memorize the rules governing the use of italicization and underlining, write a paragraph about your favorite movie. Don't forget to correctly style your favorite lines.